FINGERLINGS ™

friendship @ your fingertips

Meet the
Fingerlings

Rosie Peet

Editor Rosie Peet
Senior Designer Lisa Robb
Pre-Production Producer Kavita Varma
Producer Louise Daly
Managing Editor Paula Regan
Design Manager Jo Connor
Publisher Julie Ferris
Art Director Lisa Lanzarini
Publishing Director Simon Beecroft

First published in Great Britain in 2018 by
Dorling Kindersley Limited
80 Strand, London WC2R 0RL
A Penguin Random House Company

18 19 20 21 22 10 9 8 7 6 5 4 3 2 1
001-313507-Aug/2018

Page design copyright © 2018 Dorling Kindersley Limited
DK, a Division of Penguin Random House LLC

A CIP catalogue record for this book
is available from the British Library.

ISBN: 978-0-2413-7080-3

Printed and bound in Slovakia

www.dk.com
www.fingerlings.com

A WORLD OF IDEAS:
SEE ALL THERE IS TO KNOW

Contents

Meet the Fingerlings

These cute animals are called the Fingerlings.
They live in Melody Village.
Let's meet some of them!

Bella

This monkey is named Bella.
She lives in the treetops with
her friends.
She loves jumping and
climbing!

Boris

Boris is Bella's twin brother.

He has lots of energy.

He likes rock music.

He plays the drums loudly!

Finn

Mia

10

Hanging out

Bella and Boris have lots of monkey friends to play with.

Sophie

Zoe

Gigi

Meet Gigi the unicorn.
She loves parties with
her friends.
Gigi spreads fun wherever
she goes!

Sweet dreams

Gigi is dreaming of all her favourite things.

Glitter

Rainbows

Sweets

Taking
selfies

Fluffy clouds

15

Marge

Marge is a sloth.
She is very smart.
She likes reading books.
She also likes exploring
new places.

Kingsley

Kingsley is Marge's brother.

He is a chilled-out sloth.

He likes to relax.

His favourite hobby is surfing.

Party time

The Fingerlings love to play together.

When they play together,
the fun never stops!

Quiz

1. Where do the Fingerlings live?

2. What musical instrument does Boris play?

3. Which Fingerling loves to read?

4. Who likes surfing?

5. What kind of animal is Gigi?

6. What is the name of Bella's brother?

7. Which Fingerling loves glitter?

8. What kind of animal is Marge?

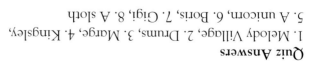

Index